C000219402

SUMMARY:

The Innovators

How a Group of Hackers, Geniuses, and
Geeks Created the Digital Revolution

ABBEY BEATHAN

Legal & Disclaimer

Table of Contents

The Book at a Glance

This book mainly focuses on how the computer and the Internet came to be. It tells us that neither the computer nor the Internet was invented by a single individual. Instead, it has been a collaborative effort among technological gurus that began way back in the 1800s.

Chapter One features Ada, Countess of Lovelace, and her interest in both poetry and mathematics. Her accomplishments were significant to the advent of computer programming.

Chapter Two talks about how the curiosity of a U.S. Census Bureau employee about improving the efficiency of census tabulation ultimately led to the invention of a computer.

Chapter Three focuses on the idea of computer scientist Alan Turing to produce a computer that would be capable of performing different tasks. In this chapter, you will learn how the computer programming industry was initially dominated by women.

Chapter Four provides a historical background of the transistor including the notable people behind it, while Chapter Five talks about the history of the microchip.

Chapter Six highlights the emergence of video games

pioneered by a group of students known as hackers. Apparently, they were the reason we have hackers in this day and age.

Chapter Seven emphasizes on the creation of the Internet and how it was initially intended for the use of private institutions, universities, and most especially by the U.S. military.

Chapter Eight talks about the impact of the hippies and techies on the emergence – and the ultimate success = of the personal computer.

Chapter Nine speaks of the history of the computer software, which was pioneered by the infamous Bill Gates.

Chapter Ten offers information on the next chapter of the Digital Revolution where the email messaging system was finally invented.

Chapter Eleven features Tim Berners-Lee and his mind-blowing innovation of the World Wide Web.

Chapter Twelve ponders on what Ada, Countess of Lovelace, would probably say with all the successful developments that transpired in the age of computers and the Internet.

In this book, you will learn that the digital age does not only include Bill Gates or Steve Jobs – there are definitely many other notable figures involved. You will learn that the success of the digital world should be attributed to the impressive teamwork of brilliant individuals.

Introduction

HOW THIS BOOK CAME TO BE

The most remarkable inventions introduced in our time include the computer and the Internet – but do we truly know who invented them? The people responsible for these creations were not solo inventors like those who get featured in the cover of business magazines. This is so because the inventions of the digital age were synergistically done by people of brilliant minds. These include entrepreneurs, inventors, hackers, and pioneers. This book is all about them – who they are, who they were, what drove them to be exceedingly creative, and how their brains worked. This book also recounts how these people realized the impact of cooperation and teamwork on their success.

In this book, author Walter Isaacson will help you understand how inventions transpire in the real world. He will talk about several significant innovations of the digital age that will make us realize that even the inventors' disturbing ideas can be turned into realities.

Mr. Isaacson will talk about cultural and social factors that drive people to push through with their innovations. For the advent of the digital age, one of these factors was a research ecosystem that was funded by the government and managed by military-industrial-academic group. Inventions of this age were also a group effort of different types of people such as hackers, hobbyists, hippies, and community organizers, among others.

Mr. Isaacson started working on this book more than a decade ago when he became fascinated with the advances brought about by the digital age. He has always had a strong interest in innovations since the time he became the biographer of Benjamin Franklin who was not only one of the Founding Fathers of the United States but was also a well-known entrepreneur, inventor, and innovator.

Aside from becoming the biographer of several notable people worldwide, Mr. Isaacson also developed a strong interest in writing about groups of people and the success of their teamwork. In fact, his first book that deviated from featuring singular individuals was "The Wise Men" which focused on the successful teamwork that led to the cold war policies of the United States. He then decided to start working on this book but had to put it on hold to finish working on the biography of Steve Jobs – which further bolstered his interest in writing a book about the evolution of the computer and the Internet. So, the moment he finished Jobs' biography, he immediately began keeping himself busy working on the story of the innovators of the digital age.

Mr. Isaacson highlights that the digital age was not a mere collaboration among peers but was a result of collaboration among people of different generations. The ideas of a group of people from one generation were shared to a group of people from another generation. This resulted in various digital innovations that included the ultimate creation of tools for communication and social networking. Then, we were introduced to artificial intelligence wherein our innovators found a way to make machines think. This expanded the definition of collaboration because the digital age has ultimately become a joint effort between machines and human beings.

Being the biographer of Steve Jobs, Mr. Isaacson had the opportunity not only to get to know one of the pioneers of the revolution of the personal computer but it was through Jobs that he learned about the fascination of several digital age innovators to correlate arts and sciences. Jobs was actually one of those innovators interested in humanities and electronics.

In fact, innovators passionate about such humanities-technology intersection have been in existence since the Renaissance period. One good example of this was painter and innovator Leonardo Da Vinci. In the 1900s, inventor Albert Einstein was also known to have a deep interest in the connection between arts and sciences. It was of public knowledge that he was fond of playing his violin while developing what we know now as the theory of relativity.

Not everyone knows Ada, the Countess of Lovelace , who lived between 1815 and 1852, and who was the daughter of poet Lord Byron who lived between 1788 and 1824. Ada did not only understand the romance of poetry but she also understood the romance of machinery and math. This is, in fact, where Mr. Isaacson intends to begin his book.

CHAPTER ONE

ADA, COUNTESS OF LOVELACE

POETICAL SCIENCE

Ada was Lord Byron's only legitimate child who had inherited his romantic spirit. In order to temper such trait, Ada's mother decided to redirect her mind to mathematics. This led to her strong interest both in writing and in mathematics. In fact, she personally described such combination as love for poetical science.

One day, Ada was invited to attend an event in London, England where she met English polymath Charles Babbage. She was extremely pleased to have attended such event as she was able to meet several scientific people. Babbage was fond of gathering poets, industrialists, writers, and other "scientists" in events such as the one where Ada was invited to. This fondness highly contributed to Babbage's popularity.

Aside from eating and drinking, his events usually featured lectures, games, readings, and dancing. The female guests would sometimes come in costumes recreating popular paintings. Astronomers would voluntarily set up telescopes while some inventors would willingly showcase their innovations. Babbage would also allow guests to check out his mechanical dolls. They did it voluntarily as it was one way of introducing their world to others and make each other interested in what others were doing.

At the event where Ada was invited for the first time, Babbage's intention was to showcase before his guests his Difference Engine innovation which had the capability to solve polynomial equations. Ada was truly impressed with such invention.

LORD BYRON

Ada apparently inherited her love for poetry and her temperament from her father but her love for machinery was definitely not from him. In fact, in 1812, Lord Byron delivered a speech expressing his disapproval of mechanical weaving machines.

One of the popular poems of Lord Byron was "Childe Harold's Pilgrimage" which talked about his adventures in Greece, Malta, and Portugal. Aside from being a famous poet, he was also known for being adventurous. At times, he would even attend three parties in a single day. In one event, he was invited in an event held by Lady Caroline Lamb – who then fell obsessively in love with Lord Byron in spite of being married to William Lamb, 2nd Viscount Melbourne.

In the same party hosted by Lady Caroline Lamb, Lord Byron also met Annabella Milbanke, who came from a multi-titled and rich family and who was simply dressed during the party. Just like other women, Annabella also found Lord Byron attractive but did not exert any effort to meet him. Nonetheless, fate allowed her not only to be introduced to him, but eventually to be married to him as well.

Unfortunately, Annabella and Lord Byron started to have a rocky marriage and even the birth of Ada in 1815 did not save their marital relationship. His infidelity caused Annabella to leave with Ada, and they never saw Lord Byron ever again. In 1824, Lord Byron died of an illness.

ADA

Ada noticeably inherited her love for poetry from her father. In an attempt to disengage her from this passion, Annabella encouraged her to develop an interest in mathematics. It was also noticeable that Ada inherited some of her father's traits such as being romantic, having mood swings, and getting easily afflicted with diseases.

One time, Annabella decided to take Ada along with her on a trip to check factories and machinery via the British industrial midlands. There, Ada saw an automated weaving loom. It impressed her that she sketched a drawing of how the machine worked. This allowed her to have a thorough understanding of how other types of machine could work = including a machine that we now call the computer.

Ada's passion for applied science was apparent and it further bolstered when she was introduced to Mary Somerville, a notable scientist and mathematician in Great Britain. When they met, Somerville had just completed her work titled "On the Connexion of the Physical Sciences" which focused on developments in various fields such as geology, botany, physics, chemistry, electricity, optics, and astronomy. They eventually developed a friendship until Somerville became Ada's mentor. The two ladies were so close that even Woronzow Greig, Somerville's son, played a significant role in Ada's marriage to William King-Noel, 1st Earl of Lovelace.

Like Ada, William also loved science but his focus was on livestock breeding techniques and crop rotation theories. After a few weeks from their initial meeting, William proposed marriage to Ada. They eventually got married in 1835. Their first born was a boy whom they named after Ada's father, Byron. Their second child was girl they named after her mother, Annabella. In spite of contracting a mysterious disease, Ada was able to give birth to their third child whom they named Ralph.

During their marriage, Ada continued to have a deep passion for mathematics and poetry. Her mathematical notes were considered to be pertinent in the computer revolution. In fact, many considered her mathematical analyses as the very first computer program ever developed.

CHAPTER TWO

THE COMPUTER

It can be said that there is perfect timing for a specific innovation. Once we are presented with a new technology, a new idea comes to mind that ultimately leads to another innovation. For example, when the development of microchips made it feasible to incorporate computer guidance systems into a rocket, the concept of taking a man to the moon soon came to mind.

However, "timing" does not always present itself outright, as in the case of the computer revolution. As early as 1800s, a paper about computer was published by Charles Babbage but it took a century to attain the real technological advances.

We have always been familiar of how railway conductors would punch holes in different places on the ticket of each passenger. This concept paved the way for innovators to analyze how punch cards could be used for computers. This concept resulted from the curiosity of Herman Hollerith, a U.S. Census Bureau employee, who was not impressed of the fact that the manual tabulation of the 1880 census literally took approximately eight years to finish. He was then determined to make the 1890 census tabulation automated.

Hollerith then decided to formulate punch cards with rows and columns that would record important details of each individual in the census such as age, height, and gender, among others. These punch cards would then be placed in a machine that would create an electric circuit for every hole. The machine was also capable of generating other data such as the number of foreign-born individuals or the number of married men. Using such technology, Hollerith succeeded in his aim of completing the 1890 census tabulation in a shorter period of one year. This breakthrough led to his decision to establish his own computer company in 1924 – which is now popularly known as IBM.

While Hollerith and his IBM could be considered as the pioneer in creating machines capable of compiling data, they could not yet be completely called computers. Thus, the emergence of more innovators and creative visionaries who were strongly driven to achieve what a real computer should be like.

DIGITAL BEATS ANALOG

During that time when Hollerith was developing his digital tabulator, brothers Lord Kelvin and James Thomson were busy developing an analog machine. The machine that the brothers were designing was capable of performing basic calculus. This system was then used by the Thomsons to develop a harmonic synthesizer. Unfortunately, their machine did not have the capability to solve more complex equations. It was only in 1931 when this issue was addressed – when Vannevar Bush, an engineering professor at MIT, developed what has been known as the very first analog electrical-mechanical computer worldwide. His machine became known as the Differential Analyzer. The success of Bush's machine led to its reproduction for several institutions including the University of Pennsylvania, the Aberdeen Proving Ground of the U.S. Army in Maryland, and the universities in Cambridge and Manchester, England.

However, because of the fact that the Differential Analyzer was an analog device, it was apparently not destined to further advance in computer history. Several theories, technologies, and approaches were introduced in the late 1930s – more than a century following the publication of Babbage's work on Analytical Engine. Nonetheless, it was during this time when four key elements were introduced – elements that were significant in defining how modern computer would be like.

These key elements include:

1. DIGITAL. One of the most essential traits of the revolution of computer was producing computers that were digital-based and not analog-based. Computer scientists discovered that using digital-based computers allow individuals to be more productive than when using analog ones. However, in 2010s, scientists once again began their research about analog computing.

2. BINARY. Scientists agreed that modern computers would not only be digital-based but the system would also be binary. This means that the digital system would only be composed of 0s and 1s — a theory founded by German polymath Gottfried Wilhelm von Leibniz.

3. ELECTRONIC. It was British engineer Tommy Flowers who introduced vacuum tubes to be used as electronic circuits' on-off switches during 1930s until researchers discovered the feasibility of electromechanical and mechanical switches for circuits. Vacuum tubes were, however, proven to be effective in running machines until they were later on replaced by transistors and microchips.

4. GENERAL PURPOSE. This key element means that the machines should be produced in such a way that it could be programmed and reprogrammed by individuals or by the machine itself. This way, the computers would be able to continuously serve its purpose.

CHAPTER THREE

PROGRAMMING

In 1948, computer scientist and mathematician Alan Turing explained a concept he had in mind – stop the production of different machines for different tasks and instead replace all of them with one single machine that would be programmed to do different tasks. Computer scientists then started to figure out ways to store programs inside the electronic memory of the computer.

GRACE HOPPER

In hindsight, we would realize that the male innovators of computers primarily concentrated on the hardware whereas those who focused on computer programming were women including Ada Lovelace. Another woman who played a significant role in the computer revolution was Grace Hopper, a math-doctorate graduate of Yale University.

While working as a professor at Vassar College, Grace encouraged her students to hone their writing skills. In fact, she would instruct her students to write essays about mathematical formulas. She emphasized that a person could never claim that he was good in math unless he could efficiently and effectively communicate it with others. This was Grace's talent – to translate scientific problems into mathematical equations and to further translate it into ordinary English. Such skill honed her to become an expert in computer programming.

In 1940s, Grace experienced boredom which eventually led to her decision to further study mathematics at New York University with mathematician Richard Courant. However, the occurrence of World War II led to changes in her life. She did not only resign as a professor of Vassar College, but she and her husband also divorced. Furthermore, she decided to join the U.S. Navy. She entered the Naval Reserve Midshipmen's School and graduated as the number one student in her class.

After graduation, Lieutenant Grace Hopper was instructed to report to Harvard University where she was tasked to work on the Mark I digital computer that was conceived by U.S. Navy commander Howard Aiken in the late 1930s. Grace then spent late nights analyzing and comprehending the blueprints. As earlier mentioned, her strengths included the capability to translate real-life problems into mathematical equations and then further translating them into common English language. As in the digital world, Grace had the capability to translate them in such a way that could be understood by the computer. With such talent, Grace provided emphasis on the fact that innovation indeed requires articulation.

Due to her exceptional skill, Aiken then instructed her to write the very first computer programming manual in world history. She completed a 500-page book that featured the Mark I history as well as its programming guidelines. Inspired by the unbuilt machine of Babbage, the Mark I was capable of being reprogrammed simply by modifying instructions.

On a daily basis, Grace would update Aiken about what she had written for the Mark I manual. They then developed a strong partnership that could be compared to the partnership of Babbage and Lovelace.

Grace also succeeded in perfecting subroutines or those codes she created for specific tasks. These were stored once in the computer but could be retrieved any time if changes were needed to be made. By mid-1940s, the Harvard Mark I became known as the very first easily programmable computer worldwide. During this time, Grace visited the University of Pennsylvania to learn more about the Electronic Numerical Integrator and Computer (ENIAC). The ENIAC was being reprogrammed and enhanced at that time, and Grace was delighted to know that the individuals in the forefront of such revolution in computer programming were women.

THE WOMEN OF ENIAC

The engineers who developed the hardware of ENIAC were all men while those responsible for the development of computer programming were six women.

Jean Jennings Bartik was one of the notable women in computer programming. She was initially enrolled at the Northwest Missouri State Teachers College as a journalism student until she decided to shift to mathematics. In 1945, she applied and got accepted for a job at the University of Pennsylvania. After several months, the university announced that there were six job vacancies wherein the chosen ones would work on the ENIAC machine. At that time, Jean had no idea what the ENIAC was but she applied for the job – and eventually got accepted. The other women who got the job were Kay McNulty Mauchly, Frances Bilas Spence, Betty Snyder Holberton, Ruth Lichterman Teitelbaum, and Marlin Wescoff Meltzer.

All of them were required to know how the IBM punch cards and plug boards worked, and so they were all sent to Aberdeen Proving Ground for six weeks of training. When they returned to the University of Pennsylvania, they were finally tasked to work on the ENIAC.

STORED PROGRAMS

From the start, electrical engineer J. Presper Eckert and physicist John Mauchly knew that there were strategies to make ENIAC more convenient to reprogram. However, they did not push through with it because it meant making a more complicated version of the hardware. Doing so might defeat ENIAC's purpose – which was to keep it simple.

Nonetheless, the duo figured out how to conveniently reprogram computers – by coming up with a computer memory that could store all computer programs. This meant developing a memory with a large capacity. Eckert then decided to apply this to the next ENIAC version wherein he would use an acoustic delay line as its storage method.

CHAPTER FOUR

THE TRANSISTOR

In spite of being invented many years ago, computers did not experience an outright revolution mainly because it was exceedingly costly for individuals to buy and own one. This is why in the first few years, computers were only seen and used by the military, research universities, and corporations.

It was costly because of the high power consumption resulting from the use of vacuum tubes. In December 1947, however, the transistor was invented by physics expert William Shockley, quantum theorist John Bardeen, and experimentalist Walter Brattain. The transistor replaced the vacuum tubes and ultimately ignited the computer revolution.

BELL LABS

Aside from the three men, Bell Labs also played a significant role in the invention of the transistor mainly because it was where it all happened.

Bell Labs was established in 1900s which consisted of engineers, metallurgists, material scientists, and theoreticians, among others. At that time, the head of its vacuum-tube department was metallurgist and physicist Mervin Kelly. He invented a water-cooling system that increased the reliability

16

of vacuum tubes but he also knew that the efficiency of tubes was only limited. In 1930s, he became the organization's research director. He was excited to begin his new post as he wanted to discover an alternative for vacuum tubes.

Bell Labs was established with a focus on practical engineering but Kelly had a wider perception of the organization. He aimed for Bell Labs to focus on theoretical research and basic science, and to become the domain of colleges and universities.

WILLIAM SHOCKLEY

William Shockley was exposed to both art and science as a child – his mother studied math and art while his father was a mine engineer and musician who could speak more than five foreign languages.

After Shockley's graduation from MIT, Kelly offered him a job – to be part of Kelly's team at Bell Labs and to find a cost-effective replacement for vacuum tubes. After three years, Shockley then discovered the feasibility of semiconductors as replacement for vacuum.

Shockley was capable of visualizing quantum theory. His colleagues would even joke that he could actually see the electrons when he looked at a semiconducting material. However, he knew he needed an experimentalist that would help him transform his insights and intuitions into real innovations – and so Walter Brattain was hired to partner with him.

Unfortunately, World War II interrupted their career at Bell Labs. Both of them eventually worked for the U.S. Navy but were assigned in different groups.

THE SOLID-STATE TEAM

During World War II, Bell Labs had to revamp its business to carry on various projects that focused on the military such as developing military communication systems and tank radio sets. The number of employees also skyrocketed to almost ten thousand.

From Manhattan, New York, Bell Labs relocated to New Jersey wherein Kelly and the rest of his team aimed to establish buildings that would give a feeling that they were like in an academic campus. So, they constructed buildings that were connected to one another and did not have segregations to encourage communication and exchange of ideas. This concept was in fact replicated by Steve Jobs for Apple's headquarters.

When the war was finally over, Shockley and Brattain went back to work for Bell Labs wherein they were assigned to continue their previous project – study the effectiveness of semiconductors as replacements for vacuum tubes. Shockley realized the need to look for a theorist – and so he hired John Bardeen who was an expert in quantum theory.

THE TRANSISTOR

With Brattain and Bardeen in his team, Shockley revived the theory he was studying long before World War II started which, unfortunately, did not work. He then asked the help of Bardeen to analyze what went wrong. It took Bardeen several months to come up with an acceptable and correct analysis.

It took Bardeen a year to come up with the photovoltaic effect theory which indicated that an electric voltage would be produced if two materials of different kind would be in contact with each other. Bardeen and Brattain collaborated to conduct experiments to prove such theory. In December 1947, the duo unveiled one of the most significant innovations of the twentieth century – the transistor.

A demonstration was then conducted by Bardeen and Brattain before Bell Labs employees. Bell Labs officers were asked to put on earphones and to take turns in using the microphone to hear the amplification of their voice using the transistor device.

CHAPTER FIVE

THE MICROCHIP

Just when the transistor celebrated its tenth anniversary in 1957, a Bell Labs executive pinpointed a problem that would possibly occur if a system was composed of tens of thousands of components – that would mean hundreds of thousands of wire links required on the circuit boards. While it definitely was not a recipe for reliability, it was nonetheless a recipe for another invention. This invention was ultimately named microchip and was a product separately developed by Fairchild Semiconductor and Texas Instruments.

JACK KILBY

Jack Kilby was working for Texas Instruments when he took part in the creation of the very first integrated circuit. Raised in Kansas City, he used to hang out with his father who managed a utility company. One time, during a severe snowstorm, a ham radio was used by him and his father to communicate with areas where their clients had lost phone service. This technology caught the interest of Jack. He was enraptured by the fact that a radio could actually have a big effect in the lives of people. He then exerted his effort to obtain his own ham operator's license. He built his own radio and continuously upgraded it. Since his younger years, he has always had an insistent curiosity about innovations.

He worked for an electronic parts manufacturer in Milwaukee. He also had the opportunity to attend a Bell Labs seminar. Until one day, he realized that he should work for a bigger company in order to augment his professional growth. In 1958, he joined Texas Instruments where he worked with Pat Haggerty, Willis Adcock, and the rest of the research team.

Most of the Texas Instruments employees were on vacation leave on the first few days that Jack reported for work. This gave him an ample time to study and come up with the different uses of silicon aside from it being used to fabricate into transistors. Two months later, he presented and demonstrated before Adcock and other executives what was considered to be the first microchip. In 1959, Texas Instruments filed for its patent and announced to the public its new innovation which they called "solid circuit."

When Robert Noyce, co-founder of Fairchild Semiconductor, learned about Texas Instruments' announcement, it bothered him as he had his own version of the same technology months before such announcement.

21

NOYCE'S VERSION

Robert and his research team began their experimentation when they learned that their transistors were not working efficiently. His research team included physicist Jean Hoerni who played a significant role in the company's efforts to come up with their own innovation.

Jean was the one who experimented with placing silicon oxide on the transistor to protect the silicon. This process was eventually called the planar process. He then further improved their innovation by engraving windows in the oxide layer that would help produce semiconductor properties. These developments prompted Robert to instruct their patent lawyer, John Ralls, to start processing their patent application. Since the job of John was to extract from the whole research team all the possible uses of their innovation, Robert was challenged to conduct further studies before they proceed with their patent application.

After a series of thorough experimentations, Robert came up with his own concept of the microchip which was considered to be better than what Jack invented for Texas Instruments. Nonetheless, it was acknowledged that the inventions of Jack and Jean both played significant roles in Robert's invention.

PROTECTING DISCOVERIES

Patents have always been challenging in the history of innovation – more so in the emergence of the digital age. Inventions result from a series of developments and collaboration of several individuals and groups, making it difficult to ascribe the extent or limitation of intellectual property rights. While there are innovators who agree to place their common invention in the public domain by going through the open-source process, there are also individual innovators who do not acknowledge the efforts of other inventors and prefer to take all the credit.

CHAPTER SIX

VIDEO GAMES

The computer revolution included the evolution of microchips which ultimately led to the production of devices that would get smaller and smaller as years passed by. Aside from that, the computer revolution also included the expansion of how the computer was used – computers should not merely be used in businesses and schools but should also be a fun device for the general public. This led to the advent of video games – which was a result of the emergence of hackers.

STEVE RUSSELL AND SPACEWAR

The "subculture of hacker" and the video game Spacewar were both products of the Tech Model Railroad Club of the MIT. It was a student organization and one of its subcommittees was called the Signals and Power Subcommittee. Its members willingly embodied the term hacker to describe themselves. According to them, a hacker is an individual who acts with ingenuity to obtain a clever outcome.

Many hackers actually came from the Artificial Intelligence Lab of MIT. It was founded by professors John McCarthy and Marvin Minsky in 1959. McCarthy was the one who came up with the term "artificial intelligence" and Minsky was the one who exceedingly believed that human intelligence will ultimately be surpassed by computers. Minsky invented a machine he called SNARC, which was short for Stochastic Neural Analog Reinforcement Calculator. It was an invention that intended to model the brain. His theory was that small computers, if connected by a network, would result in intelligence.

In 1961, a significant moment was experienced by Tech Model Railroad Club hackers when the Digital Equipment Corporation (DEC) decided to donate its PDP-1 computer prototype to MIT in September. It was the very first computer with the capability of directly interacting with the user.

A group of hackers then called themselves the Hingham Institute. They were the ones who thoroughly studied the features of the PDP-1 computer not to analyze how they could further improve a computer but simply to have fun and discover clever things that could be done with it – until they realized that a real video game could be created using the PDP-1.

Steve Russell was considered to be the group's best

programmer. At that time, he was assisting Professor McCarthy in creating the LISP computer programming language that intended to expedite research on artificial intelligence. He was obsessed with the works of author E.E. Doc Smith who mainly focused on space opera, a sci-fi subgenre often described as trashy.

Steve, Martin Graetz, and their friends shared the same passion for space operas that's why it did not come as a surprise when they were able to create a space-war video game for the PDP-1. They sought the help of their fellow Alan Kotok to solve other issues that were beyond the capabilities of Steve and Martin. Then, from December 1961 to February 1962, Steve hacked away until he completed the basic features of the video game. Since it was a collaboration of several hackers, Spacewar was considered to be an open-source project.

As time went by, several enhancements were done to Spacewar while the computer world continued to revolutionize. This included the production of remote controls after Alan and Bob had observed how awkward it was to directly use the console to play.

Spacewar paved the way to the success of the digital age. It became the instrument in the discovery of the key ingredients of the computer revolution. First, collaboration in its truest sense is significant. Second, it introduced free and open-source computer software. Third, computers should be used by everyone at work, in school, and for fun.

NOLAN BUSHNELL AND ATARI

Nolan Bushnell was one of those computer science students who became obsessed with Spacewar. This made him look up to Steve. Aside from being a computer addict, he made sure he had time to work at an amusement park as it was his source of money to pay for college. At a young age, he was already displaying an attitude of an entrepreneur – he was both a risk-taker and a thrill-seeker. This attitude successfully allowed him to transform one invention into an entire industry.

CHAPTER SEVEN

THE INTERNET

VANNEVAR BUSH'S TRIANGLE

When we talk about inventions, these are often introduced to the public with the trademark of the organizations or individuals that created them. This is, however, not the case with the Internet because it was developed through collaboration among private institutions, universities, and the military. Such unity among the three groups was the outcome of World War II.

MIT professor Vannevar Bush played a major role in the establishment of such assemblage as he was one of the most, if not the most, credible figures to do such task. At that time, he was the School of Engineering dean at MIT; he was a top administrator of the U.S. military science during the war, and he founded the Raytheon electronics company. Similar to most technology leaders, he grew up with utmost passion for both sciences and humanities.

He obtained his doctorate in electrical engineering from Harvard and MIT. He soon became the engineering dean and a professor at MIT where he invented the Differential Analyzer. During World War II, he became concerned about the likelihood that the U.S. military might soon be outdated in terms of technology. So he successfully encouraged scientific leaders to unite in convincing U.S. President Franklin Roosevelt to establish groups that would focus on this matter. This led to the creation of the Office of Scientific Research and Development of the U.S. military and the U.S. National Defense Research Committee = he was then tasked to head both. Soon thereafter, he ordered the research, production, and development of atom bombs, radars, and air-defense systems. His success as the head of these groups earned him the title "General of Physics," as described by "Times" magazine in 1944. After World War II, he was instructed by Roosevelt to write a report about the establishments of his groups – it was titled "Science, the Endless Frontier." Indeed, the technological revolution that bolstered in the twentieth century started from the establishment of the triangular relationship among academia, industry, and government.

J.C.R. LICKLIDER

Joseph Carl Robnett "Lick" Licklider was known as one of the fathers of the Internet. He was the pioneer of the Internet's two most significant and underlying concepts which included the decentralization of networks for the distribution of information everywhere, and the interfaces

29

that would be responsible for expediting real time human-machine interaction. He headed the military office that provided the funds for the ARPANET and later on for the Internet.

Lick obtained his doctorate in psychoacoustics at Washington University and eventually joined the psychoacoustics lab of Harvard. He was exceedingly interested in learning more about the relationship of technology and psychology, and to be able to do so, he decided to join MIT where he established a psychology section within the Electrical Engineering Department.

Lick also had passion for art and this allowed him to become more intuitive. It gave him the ability to process information and study patterns, which were significant in the development of the Internet.

TIME-SHARING AND MAN-COMPUTER SYMBIOSIS

In 1950s, Lick and McCarthy collaborated at MIT to develop computer systems for time-sharing. The goal was to have a single mainframe with sufficient memory that could monitor all users. This, of course, also required a reliable operating system that could run programs and multitask.

At Lincoln Laboratory, Lick created a team of engineers and psychologists which manifested the unmistakable significance of interactive computing. He wanted the team to enhance human-machine interaction using friendly interface.

In 1960, Lick published a paper that focused on postwar technology titled "Man-Computer Symbiosis." Perhaps, today, there is no need to read this paper anymore because the concepts indicated there are those that form part of the technology that we are using today in the digital age.

Between artificial intelligence that McCarthy and Minsky introduced and the theory of cybernetics that Norbert Wiener worked on, Lick was more in favor of Wiener's theory. This is because the theory of cybernetics highlighted the close collaboration between humans and machines.

CHAPTER EIGHT

THE PERSONAL COMPUTER

"AS WE MAY THINK"

It was Bush who envisioned how a personal computer should look like. In 1945, he wrote an article titled "As We May Think" for the publication "Atlantic." There, he mentioned the feasibility of inventing a personal machine that would have the capability to store all types of information including pictures, books, and records, among many others. He even envisioned the development of file sharing and hypertext links. At that time, he called such personal machine as "memex." His team then continued to study how this would all be possible.

However, as years went by, the way Bush envisioned computers was not how things turned out to be. Computers were not used as a personal device but were instead created exclusively for the use of the military and of different industries. In simpler terms, computers were not for individual use.

In 1974, members of the DEC operations committee were still arguing whether or not a computer should be developed for personal consumers. This debate that seemed endless and hopeless paved the way for new entrepreneurs to emerge. They were the ones who produced and believed in the feasibility of selling personal computers to individuals. They were young entrepreneurs who ran their startup businesses in garages and strip malls. These businesses included Apple and Altair. It was indeed the start of the revolution of personal computers.

THE CULTURAL BREW

What contributed to the development of the personal computer was a combination of technological advances – most specifically the invention of the microprocessor which integrated all of the central processing unit's functions.

Aside from geeks and hackers that had contributed to the computer revolution since day one, the computer world was joined by new generations, new cultures, and different types of personalities. This included hippies, New Left activists, and Whole Earth communalists which were highly interested in do-it-yourself creativity. These groups wanted to produce personal computers to free them from the restrictions imposed by academic, corporate and government institutions.

Soon, there was the emergence of a technotribalism. These people whose interests and values are similar to one another soon found themselves meeting on a regular basis which

33

included technology gurus Marshall McLuhan, Richard Brautigan, Buckminster Fuller, and Norbert Wiener.

STEWART BRAND

At that time, Stewart Brand could be considered as the most buoyant individual when it came to promoting the association between hippies and techies. He mentioned in his essay "We Owe It All to the Hippies," which was published in the journal "Time" in 1995, the impact of counterculture on the philosophical foundations of the revolution of the entire personal computer industry worldwide. He wrote that modern cyberrevolution was established due to libertarian politics and hippie communalism.

Just like the other tech gurus, Stewart was also a ham radio operator. But aside from that, he was also a technician, photographer, and producer of the USCO multimedia art collective. USCO was a producer of events that involved projected images, strobe lights, technological wizardry, and acid rock music. At times, USCO would conduct talks featuring speakers of the new age including Dick Alpert and Marshall McLuhan. Events as such strengthened the link between technology and mysticism – and thus strengthened their link with communication and introspection. For these hippies, technology was perceived as an instrument of expression that could bolster creativity. Hippies were considered rebellious individuals and, for them, technology was tantamount to freedom. Technology eliminated the limitations of life.

In 1960s, the slogan "Power to the people" was used in a protest by the political activists of the New Left. Stewart and other tech gurus then believed that the slogan was more apt if used in the computer industry because there was no doubt that the society was positively changed by the advent of computers more than what the society had become due to politics.

CHAPTER 9

SOFTWARE

In 1975, Paul Allen got hold of the magazine "Popular Electronics" and became excited about the emergence of the personal computer industry. At the same time, he badly wanted to be part of this revolution so he visited his good friend, Bill Gates, and told him that they could not simply allow the personal computer revolution to happen without them. Soon thereafter, they thoroughly studied code writing that would ultimately change the computer world.

Gates was not interested in computer hardware as he and Allen specialized in software. So, when they learned about the personal computer revolution, their goal was to develop software for those personal computers. The intention of Gates and Allen was to make the hardware an interchangeable product – this meant more profits for the developers of the operating system and software. At that time, the computer software industry was non-existent.

BILL GATES

As a child, Gates was engaged in sports like tennis and water ski, and he loved to spend time with friends and family. But his parents also knew that he was not a typical child – more specifically, he was not the typical student in class as he had noticeably extreme intellect. Once, his fourth-grade teacher instructed the class to write a five-page essay but what Gates submitted was a thirty-page paper. His interests were not similar to the interests of children of his age, and so his parents decided to move him to a private school. He then transferred to Lakeside School.

At the science and math building of Lakeside, his seventh-grade teacher in math showed him a Teletype terminal linked to a time-sharing computer system using a telephone line. He started visiting the computer room as often as he could on a daily basis – sometimes he would bring his friends – to explore the machine. It was using the BASIC computer language, or the Beginner's All-purpose Symbolic Instruction Code. The teachers at Lakeside did not have any knowledge about BASIC but Gates and his friends patiently read the BASIC manual and even did further reading about it.

Allen was two years older than Gates but they developed a friendship because they always saw each other in the computer room. Allen was in awe when he visited the Gates' home and learned that Gates read the "Fortune" magazine regularly. Allen had known him to be a truly competitive, persistent, and focused person. While Allen's nature was to flit from one idea to another, Gates was the opposite. Gates

37

would share one big idea, focus on it, and work on it with total discipline until he mastered it.

As early as the seventh grade, Gates was already telling his friends that by the age of thirty, he was going to make a million U.S. dollars. Well, he was wrong. He did not accurately predict that by the age of thirty, his worth would be three hundred fifty million U.S. dollars.

THE LAKESIDE PROGRAMMING GROUP

Gates and Allen decided to establish the Lakeside Programming Group in 1968 where they discussed anything related to computers and their other interests. Soon, the group highly focused on discussing moneymaking businesses.

In 1968, the group was tasked by C-Cubed to place Lakeside's machine under "stress test." Gates and the rest of the group would use it as often as they wanted, even during weekends, and use up all its memory to achieve the goal – to make the machine crash. They just had to make sure that they could explain what they did that resulted to the crash.

In return, they were allowed to use the facilities of C-Cubed. This enabled them to have the opportunity to write computer programs. They created video games such as Monopoly and war games, among others. They spent most of their time there in front of computers and the only time they would be seen outside the premises was when they felt hungry. They would usually hang out at Morningtown Pizza, a pizza parlor frequented by hippies.

CHAPTER 10

ONLINE

In 1970s, both the personal computer and the Internet were born. The aim of some innovators was to make them grow together but then they eventually grew apart and experienced successes separate from each other. This transpired as there were tech gurus who were only excited about networking and there were those who only wanted to focus on personal computer.

It was only in 1980s when the growth of both personal computers and the Internet began to intertwine. It was the start of another chapter of the Digital Revolution.

EMAIL AND BULLETIN BOARDS

ARPANET was created to serve as a network mainly intended for time-sharing computer resources but it unfortunately failed to serve such purpose. Instead, it became a tool for communications, including social networking. It was considered to be the technical foundation of the success of the Internet. However, the sad truth about the digital revolution is that the aspiration to continuously improve communication, connection, collaboration, and the establishment of community would imminently kill old computer applications in favor of the new ones. In the case of the ARPANET, the birth of the email had a huge impact on its success.

Prior to the massive success of the Internet worldwide, electronic mail was already being adapted and studied by researchers who were working on time-sharing computers at that time. Using a computer program they called SNDMSG, they discovered that a computer user could be capable of sending messages to the personal folder of another user of the same computer. MIT engineer Ray Tomlinson then thought of a hack that would allow a computer user to send messages to the personal folder of a user of another computer and another mainframe. He created a file transfer program he dubbed as CPYNET and combined it with SNDMSG. This allowed the exchanges of files between two computers using the ARPANET. To ensure that the messages would be sent to the intended recipient, he invented an addressing system wherein the @ sign was used. The popular format of email addresses – username@hostname – that we have always known was in fact Tomlinson's creation. He made the @ sign the iconic symbol of connecting everyone around the world.

There were still researchers assigned to further investigate the feasibility of ARPANET as a network for time-sharing computing resources but the excitement to push through with it died down due to the extreme excitement of everyone about the email messaging system. Even ARPANET director Stephen Lukasik became addicted to the capabilities of email.

Through continuous research, it was discovered how email did not only allow two users to exchange messages. The formation of virtual communities was also discovered. Email chains were used to check the feasibility if the intended recipients would successfully receive the messages. The email recipients belonged to a group of subscribers which eventually termed as "mailing list."

The SF-Lovers was the very first major mailing list and was composed of science fiction lovers. At one point, the officers wanted to abolish the SF-Lovers lest a political figure would have the wrong notion that government money was being used to support the unrelated activities of sci-fi fans. However, they all saw the significance of such virtual community. This paved the way for the formation of online communities one after another.

However, in spite of such discoveries, it was not very popular among consumers mainly because even if they were owners of personal computers, they still had to find ways to connect.

42

MODEMS

In 1980s, the modem device was invented allowing home computers and international networks to connect. It could produce analog signals through a telephone circuit in order to send and receive digital data. This was the beginning of the online revolution.

However, the fact that during that time, AT&T was somewhat operating a near-monopoly business, the online communication business was running slow. Nonetheless, the digital age was posing both an advantage and a disadvantage to the company. On one hand, AT&T was given the opportunity to expand or enhance their products and services. On the other hand, there were other businessmen who also saw the opportunity to offer something new to consumers. AT&T then started to face big competition.

Stewart Brand had always been present in each phase of the digital period, and in the age of virtual communication, he was involved in the formation of the experimental online community called The WELL.

CHAPTER ELEVEN

THE WEB

In spite of the emergence of online services and modems, the popularity of the Internet was nonetheless limited during 1980s. Until more and more tech gurus became involved in the digital revolution, various methods of online communication services began to emerge in early 1990s. Older versions of online communication became obsolete and the idealistic dreams of Engelbart, Licklider and Bush were all surpassed. The stupefying developments in the digital age were even further strengthened by Tim Berners-Lee, the man who introduced the World Wide Web.

TIM BERNERS-LEE

The parents of Tim Berners-Lee were both computer scientists, hence, his exposure to computers. At an early age, Tim already believed that nothing was impossible. He once said in an interview that the limitations on what could be done with a computer were mere limitations of the imagination.

He loved getting hold of broken devices and learning to make them work on his own. He once salvaged a broken calculator which he was able to transform into an elemental computer.

He then acquired a broken TV set which he repaired and used as his computer monitor.

He then studied microprocessors and started to have a thorough understanding of electronics. He and his friends could make boards and they could sell it too but they were from Oxfordshire, England – where people were not as aggressive as those who were in Silicon Valley.

In his younger years, there was an almanac and advice book titled "Enquire Within Upon Everything" in his family home. Its introduction section enumerated various topics that could be found inside the book including domestic life, headache treatment, event planning, and the rules of etiquette, among many others. By the late 1800s, the book had 89 editions already and over a million copies were sold. Tim observed how successful such book was as it was sold worldwide and contained a world of information. It was the start of how he envisioned the creation of the World Wide Web.

Since childhood, Tim had always been curious about the capability of the human brain to do random associations of one object to another or one incident to another. This, he said, could not be done by machines as they could only make associations that they would be programmed to make. He was fascinated of the fact that people could work together –

for instance, an individual could probably have half of the solution to a problem while another individual could have the other half. He was fascinated of how one person could finish the statement of another person. He had also observed how people love to brainstorm. Once, he asked himself how this could be done by people miles away from each other. After his graduation from Oxford, he badly wanted to find answers to his questions.

He then accepted a job at CERN where he was tasked to monitor thousands of researchers and their corresponding projects as well as their computer systems. This led to his development of a computer program he called Enquire. His curiosity was once ignited, toying with the viability of having similar information accessible through all computers wherever people may be. He was envisioning one global information space. At that time though, he was not aware that his ideas were similar to the memex machine of Van Bush.

His contract as a consultant at CERN expired so he looked for another work in England. However, he found his job boring so he went back to CERN to apply for a fellowship. In 1984, he was given the opportunity to join a group of individuals whose job was to gather study results. He loved the way individuals worked at CERN and this once again ignited his fascination for people working together. He

46

wanted to find a way how collaboration and brainstorming could be done and ultimately be preserved even if people were not in one room – or in one country. So, he began his quest on how to revamp and further enhance his Enquire program.

Since there was already the Internet, Tim was playing with the idea of making information available online and linking related topics with each other. He was able to make this happen with the help of his invention, the hypertext.

The hypertext is what everyone knows today as a word or phrase that forms part of an online document which when clicked will redirect the user to another related document. This was a concept that was also envisioned by Van Bush and another technology visionary Ted Nelson in 1960s but failed to come into fruition. Tim apparently was able to make it happen.

Tim then began to work on this project. He used a NeXT computer – an innovation of the notable Apple Inc. co-founder Steve Jobs – to work on his Remote Procedure Call protocol that could allow a computer's program to call up another computer's subroutine. He created the Universal Document Identifiers which was eventually renamed as Uniform Resource Locators due to an issue involving the members of the Internet Engineering Task Force. These locators are what we now familiarly call URLs. He also created the Hypertext Transfer Protocol (HTTP) and the Hypertext Markup Language (HTML) that we are all very familiar of in this day and age.

In 1989, Tim decided to request for funding from CERN to turn all his ideas into reality, and so he presented his funding proposal to the top management. Unfortunately, it was rejected because the officers found Tim's proposal vague.

Had Tim had the money, he could be considered as the only person to have conceived of the Web. However, the only way he could think of in order to make his ideas become a reality was to obtain financial assistance. Good thing he met CERN engineer Robert Cailliau who successfully helped him polish his funding proposal. Cailliau made sure that the proposal would remain to be interesting and exciting but he also made sure that he eliminated its vagueness.

Cailliau said that Tim needed a catchy title for the funding proposal. After toying with different titles such as Information Management, Mine of Information, and The Information Mine, among others, they finally settled for this:

"WorldWideWeb: Proposal for a HyperText Project." Hence, the birth of the term "Web."

CHAPTER TWELVE

ADA FOREVER

LADY LOVELACE'S OBJECTION

If Ada Lovelace could only see everything that transpired in the Digital Revolution, she would probably be happy and grateful that the ideas she came up with hundreds of years ago had a major contribution to the success of the computer and the Internet industries.

Among the remarkable innovations that bolstered our way of living are the microchips and packet-switched networks. These allowed the transformation of computers from big machines to small personal gadgets that are all capable of being connected to one another on a web.

In 1960s, the movie "2001: A Space Odyssey," directed by Stanley Kubrick featured an intelligent computer named HAL. Ada, during her time, did not believe that such computer could ever be invented. However, there are many technology gurus today that are focusing on studies on artificial intelligence who aim to prove her wrong.

In 1956, artificial intelligence was already introduced at a conference conducted by Marvin Minsky and John McCarthy at Dartmouth College in New Hampshire. The participants concluded that artificial intelligence would experience a breakthrough after twenty years. It has been more than twenty years and it still is an ongoing work in progress.

John von Neumann, prior to his death in 1957, was conducting his thorough study of artificial intelligence. His extensive participation in the innovation of the personal computer made him realize how far different the human brain is from the architecture of computers. He once stated that perhaps the digital approach should not be the only method applied in studying the future of intelligent computing. Perhaps, both analog and digital methods should be applied to turn ideas into realities.

Frank Rosenblatt, a professor at Cornell University, also attempted to come up with a mathematical approach in 1958 to develop an artificial neural network with similar features as that of the human brain – dubbed as the Perceptron. However, up until now, the Perceptron has not existed although there are researchers that continue to study its viability.

IBM chief executive officer Ginni Rometty believes that the artificial intelligence community was awakened by two incidents. First, IBM invented a chess-playing machine that emerged victorious after playing with world champion Garry

Kasparov. Second, a question-answering computer won at the television game show "Jeopardy!" after playing with champions Ken Jennings and Brad Rutter. However, these could not be totally considered breakthroughs of artificial intelligence – they only look like they are. As Berkeley professor of philosophy John Searle explained it, such kind of computers would never be able to understand. They only seemed to understand because of the myriad of information stored in their memory. IBM research director John E. Kelly III also once stated that computers would never be able to interact, adapt, learn, or understand the way humans do. Indiana University professor Douglas Hofstadter mentioned in the book he released in 1979 that researchers needed to study the way human imagination worked in order to shed light on how to make artificial intelligence work.

Conclusion

This book sheds light on the history of the Internet and the computer. It enlightens us how efficient collaboration can ultimately lead to success. All the technology gurus and visionaries featured in this book are indeed credible proof of the real essence of teamwork and cooperation. Had they not willingly shared their ideas and expertise with each other, we probably would not experience the enjoyment and convenience we experience now brought about by computers and Internet.

This book is recommended to everyone mainly because everyone doubtlessly uses computers and the Internet in this day and age. Surely, everyone will understand and learn a big deal from this book. Moreover, there is likelihood that some readers will even be inspired to conduct their own research and form part of the Digital Revolution – after all, there is probably a myriad of innovations out there still waiting to be discovered, specifically in the field of humanlike artificial intelligence.

This book is particularly recommended to those who believe that inventions can only be achieved by singular geniuses. As earlier mentioned, this book opens our eyes on the big impact of cooperation on success.

This book is, of course, highly recommended to technology enthusiasts. There are indeed a whole lot of things to learn from this book in terms of the Digital Revolution.

This book is truly inspiring to also exert an effort and be able to come up with our own inventions that will help improve lives.

Final Thoughts

Hey! Did you enjoy this book? We sincerely hope you thoroughly enjoyed this short read and have gotten immensely valuable insights that will help you in any areas of your life.

Would it be too greedy if we ask for a review from you?

It takes 1 minute to leave 1 review to possibly influence 1 more person's decision to read just 1 book which may change their 1 life. Your 1 minute matters and we value it and thank you so much for giving us your 1 minute. If it sucks, just say it sucks. Period.

FREE BONUS

P.S. Is it okay if we overdeliver?

Here at Abbey Beathan Publishing, we believe in overdelivering way beyond our reader's expectations. Is it okay if we overdeliver?

Here's the deal, we're going to give you an extremely valuable cheatsheet of "Accelerated Learning". We've partnered up with Ikigai Publishing to present to you the exclusive bonus of "Accelerated Learning Cheatsheet"

What's the catch? We need to trust you… You see, we want to overdeliver and in order for us to do that, we've to trust our reader to keep this bonus a secret to themselves. Why? Because we don't want people to be getting our exclusive accelerated learning cheatsheet without even buying our books itself. Unethical, right?

Ok. Are you ready?

Simply Visit this link: http://bit.ly/acceleratedcheatsheet

We hope you'll enjoy our free bonuses as much as we've enjoyed preparing it for you!

Free Bonus #2: Free Book Preview of
Summary: The Daily Stoic
The Book at a Glance

Stoicism is a philosophy which dates back to the ancient times. It is often defined as the study by which we learn how to deal with hardships by understanding what things are within our control, and by sufficiently preparing for possible difficulties ahead. This is achieved through developing an indifference towards earthly desires, which eventually provides us with peace of mind and happier lives. Simply stated, it is a philosophy which helps us live a good life by choosing to do and be good.

From the definition alone, stoicism can seem like a complicated philosophy that can only be embraced by people with a certain degree of intelligence. Fortunately, stoicism is for everyone.

The Daily Stoic by Ryan Holiday and Stephen Hanselman aims to provide us with ways by which we can learn and embrace this philosophy on a daily basis. This book lists down 366 notes for meditation which is perfect for daily reflections.

This book is divided into three parts, representing the three disciplines of Stoicism, with each part divided equally into four chapters – a total of 12 chapters representing each month of the year.

The first part of this book is all about the discipline of perception. In the first chapter, for the month of January, we are taught all about creating clarity within our own minds. In the month of February, we are given daily messages to meditate upon in order to gain control over our passions and emotions. The author also adds a 29th message in case of leap years. For March, we are taught about developing an awareness about how the world works. In chapter four, we are encouraged to develop unbiased thoughts through exercises and meditations which will last all throughout the month of April.

The second part of this book discusses the discipline of action. For the fifth month, we will be tackling ways on how our choices lead to doing the right action. In chapter six, the author provides us with tips on how we become better at solving our problems. In chapter seven, the whole month of July is dedicated towards developing a sense of duty within us. And finally, chapter eight will teach us how to live pragmatically.

And finally, the last part of the book will teach us the discipline of will. The teachings start with chapter nine, where we are taught to build resilience, fortitude, and inner strength. In chapter ten, we focus on the month of October, where we gain a deeper understanding of our virtues of justice and self-control. But more importantly, we also learn about kindness – and that it is something that lies within us. Chapter eleven is all about acceptance. In this chapter, the author dedicates the whole month of November to teach us to accept only the things that are within our control. And finally, chapter twelve will help us meditate on our mortality. This means that the whole month of December will be an eye-opener about how fleeting life can be.

But above all, the author hopes that this book will serve as our daily guide towards living the good life. And in order to live it, we must actually stand up and face the world with these principles as our guiding light.

Introduction

All of us experience stress and hardships. What we don't know is that we ourselves are responsible for making ourselves suffer in the first place. Fortunately, stoicism is here to help us move past and conquer our problems.

When people hear "stoicism", they immediately think of ancient greats like Marcus Aurelius and Cato the Younger, or former presidents like George Washington and Theodore Roosevelt. This makes them feel that you have to meet certain qualifications first in order to become Stoic. However, this is not the case.

In this book, the author lists down the ways by which we, too, can embrace stoicism in our everyday lives. Keep in mind that stoicism is a philosophy which helps us overcome obstacles, and certainly, all of us have obstacles to face for which it will come in handy.

As you read through this book, you will realize that stoicism is not only a war philosophy, but something we can embrace in our day to day lives. But in order to fully embrace this philosophy, we must take things slow. Each chapter in this book will represent a month, and each discussion is what you will reflect on in that specific day. Thus, there is no rush into reading everything at once. After all, true learning is not measured by how many books you've read. Instead, it is measured by how well you were able to understand what a book is trying to convey.

January: Clarity

January 1ˢᵗ

For the first day of the year, we must learn how to identify the things which fall under our control, on those which do not. Once we are able to do so, we must shift our focus towards the things we can change. Keep in mind that when we focus too much on the things which we cannot change, we end up spending time and effort on the wrong things – and as a result, we end up feeling stressed out and unhappy in the long run.

January 2ⁿᵈ

Often, we think that books are simply written to provide us with entertainment during our spare time. Instead of looking at them as mere objects, we should try to look at them as sources of wisdom and learning. They must be seen as tools to provide us with further education – that they have a purpose. When we think of them in this way, then we won't be easily distracted by unnecessary activities. Additionally, the knowledge we acquire will help set us free.

January 3ʳᵈ

For the third day, the author wants us to say "no" to the things that don't matter. We are all familiar with regret-filled instances when we said "yes" to something that we don't really want to do – and this is exactly what the author wants us to avoid. When we finally say "no" to requests we don't want to do, we shift our focus towards accomplishing the things which truly matter in our lives.

The author understands that it may hurt a few people in the process, and that may cause you to think twice about saying no. When this happens, keep in mind that what you are living in is your own life. You deserve to enjoy it on your own terms.

January 4th

For this day, the author simply wants to share that Stoic philosophy only has three essential disciplines which can help us with our day-to-day lives. The first is to have the ability to control our perceptions, the second is to be able to properly direct our actions, and the last one is to have the will to accept that certain things are beyond our control.

January 5th

At this point, we must understand the need to have clear goals for the future. This, however, does not mean that we simply need a goal – instead, it must be a goal that's clearly defined by us. Without being clear with our intentions and goals, then we spend each day wandering aimlessly and achieving nothing at all.

January 6th

The questions of "who", "what", "where", and "why" are often thrown our way, so we never really thought about answering them with a deeper perspective. The author encourages us to pause for a while and think about giving substantive answers to these questions. This will provide us with clarity as to who we truly are, and what we want to do in life.

January 7th

In order to dive deeper into clarity, the author wants us to know that the mind only has seven functions. These functions are as follows:

- Choice, the ability to do and think what's right

- Refusal, the ability to reject any form of temptation

- Yearning, the ability to hope for the better

- Repulsion, the ability to lean away from negativity and other bad influences

- Preparation, the ability to be ready for what lies ahead

- Purpose, the ability to have guiding principles and to determine priorities

- Assent, the ability to accept what is – and what isn't – within our control.

Beyond these seven functions, we must already consider them as pollution or corruption: thought processes which do more harm than good.

January 8th

Sometimes, we may think that minor indulgences are harmless. However, these indulgences can cloud our clarity and, as a result, they can spiral out of control and turn into serious addictions. To prevent this from happening, we must regain control of our desires and abstain. When we are capable of abstaining from our addictions, we gain control of our lives.

January 9th

At this point, we are now aware that there are certain things we cannot control. For today, the author encourages us to refrain from controlling the external events that happen. And instead of controlling the situation itself, we try to control what we think about it instead. This exercise will help us focus on our inner control which, in turn, helps us develop clarity around the things that truly matter: what's inside our minds.

January 10th

Stoic philosophy helps us live steady, stable, and tranquil lives. In order to achieve this, we must use our reason to filter out the outside world. But before doing so, we must make sure that our reason is not polluted or corrupted by the external world. Otherwise, we cannot experience clarity, and internal chaos will ensue.

January 11th

We previously learned that serenity and stability results from our choices based on reason. However, we must not completely shut away all disruptions. Instead, we must distinguish between disruptive events and disruptive judgments. The former is a normal part of life, while the latter is a thought process which can cause more problems. Thus, what we must truly avoid are disruptive judgments.

January 12th

As soon as you wake up today, remind yourself of the things you can control, and the things you can't. Throughout the day, the author encourages us to continually remind ourselves that we are responsible for making our own choices, and that there are certain things which are beyond our control. And as we prepare for bed, we must keep in mind that sleep is a form of surrender, which helps us prepare for a whole new day.

January 13th

The author states that the only thing that matters is what's inside of our circle of control: our mind. Aside from helping us narrow down what we're responsible for, it also helps us focus on the things that matter. In contrast, those who do not know what's inside the circle of control are more prone to making corrupt choices, and being busy with irrelevant matters.

January 14th

To truly live the life we want, we must be free from external temptations. These temptations have various forms, like gambling, gaming apps, gossip, and other similar time-consuming activities. To fight them, we must develop an awareness of what truly matters for us, and carefully cut the strings of those which are simply trying to lure us into their trap. Otherwise, we will turn into their puppets.

January 15th

The secret to attaining clarity is by living in tranquility; and in order to do so, we must get rid of any self-doubt. More importantly, we must trust that the path we're on is the right one, and ignore all other distractions which we encounter along the way.

January 16*th*

The study of this philosophy aims to get rid of routine behavior. In order to do so, we must identify the habits that we have already formed. As a guide, the author wants us to reflect on these questions: "why do we do what we do?" and "is this the best way to do it?"

January 17*th*

For today, the author wants to remind us that success or failure is not defined by the grades or trophies we received. Instead, it is defined by the quality of life you have. We must reflect on that first before anything else.

January 18*th*

We must learn to see the beauty in the ordinary. This helps change our perspective from something dark and depressing to something that is filled with joy, light, and clarity.

January 19*th*

Wherever we are in life, one thing remains constant: we have freedom of choice. Knowing this helps us focus only on things that we have control over. Once we understand that, we become closer to achieving clarity

January 20th

Today, the author wants us to know that the choice is ours to restart whenever we feel like life is being problematic. After all, everything that had happened – even if it just happened five minutes ago – is all in the past now. Choose to move forward and simply restart life.

January 21st

From today onwards, the author wants us to start each day with a morning ritual. This will help us reflect on what's happening inside us, and will serve as a guide for how we make choices and live our lives. We can do so in different forms like meditation, exercise, or journaling – whatever makes us feel more connected with our inner self will do.

January 22nd

Stoics keep journals where they write down their thoughts and reviews about their thoughts and actions. For them, this was a way to develop personal clarity. The author encourages us to do the same.

January 23rd

We should keep reminding ourselves that money will never be able to solve internal issues. The solution will show itself only when we finally attain clarity.

January 24th

When we read, we must not only scan each page with our eyes. Instead, we must absorb each line, and try to understand what it is trying to convey. This deep reading is what the author wants us to develop, and that is why he only provides us with brief passages for each day.

January 25th

When we develop clarity, we also develop prioritization, since we already know which ones matter for us. This can help us stay focused on doing what we love most, and that alone can guarantee that we will enjoy our lives. After all, the more time we spend on superficial desires, the less time we're spending on those that make us happy.

January 26th

A mantra is a word or phrase which provides us with clarity and spiritual guidance. For today, the author encourages us to create a mantra which can help us find clarity, and stick to it.

January 27th

In order to attain clarity and success, there are only three areas of training that we must focus on: first is to decide what we want and what we don't want, second is to observe our motivations, and the last is to observe our judgment and reason. When we realize that these areas are interconnected, we become a step closer to attaining clarity.

January 28th

For today, the author wants us to pick a role model. This should be a person that you're really looking up to. And, whenever you encounter a problem, ask yourself what that person would – or wouldn't do. Then, try to do the same.

January 29th

Each day, we can be overwhelmed by distractions and problems. Keep in mind that we have the choice to steer clear from these distractions. Choose to stay focused on the things that truly matter – it's really as simple as that.

January 30th

We are living in a highly connected world, and that makes information available at the tip of our fingers. This can make us feel like we have to be on top of everything. However, the author shares that there is no concrete evidence that we have to be so. He reminds us that when we try to be on top of things all the time, we end up consuming our time, energy, and brainpower on trivial matters.

January 31st

Stoicism is like our soul's medicine. Aside from helping us focus on what we have to do, it also helps us restore the energy we need in order to attain our goals. Knowing this is enough to keep us going on this journey.

Read More...

72

CPSIA information can be obtained
at www.ICGtesting.com
Printed in the USA
BVHW041050260619
552020BV00001B/62/P